88TH CONGRESS, 2D SESSION, HOUSE DOCUMENT NO. 279

The Yearbook of Agriculture

1964

THE UNITED STATES GOVERNMENT PRINTING OFFICE